MILES MORALES: THE ULTIMATE SPIDER-MAN REVIVAL

KU-072-207

MILES MORALES: ULTIMATE SPIDER-MAN #1-7

WRITER: **BRIAN MICHAEL BENDIS**
ARTIST: **DAVID MARQUEZ**
COLOURIST: **JUSTIN PONSOR** with **JASON KEITH (ISSUE #6)**
LETTERER: **VC'S CORY PETIT**
COVER ART: **FIONA STAPLES**

Do you have any comments or queries about Miles Morales: Ultimate Spider-Man - Revival? Email us at graphicnovels@panini.co.uk
Join us on Facebook at Panini/Marvel Graphic Novels

© 2018 Marvel

TM & © 2018 Marvel & Subs. Licensed by Marvel Characters B.V. through Panini S.p.A., Italy. All Rights Reserved. First impression 2018. Published by Panini Publishing, a division of Panini UK Limited. Mike Riddell, Managing Director. Alan O'Keefe, Managing Editor. Mark Irvine, Production Manager. Marco M. Lupoi, Publishing Director Europe. Jason Quinn, Reprint Editor. Charlotte Harvey, Designer. Office of publication: Brockbourne House, 77 Mount Ephraim, Tunbridge Wells, Kent TN4 8BS. This publication may not be sold, except by authorised dealers, and is sold subject to the condition that it shall not be sold or distributed with any part of its cover or markings removed, nor in a mutilated condition. Printed in the United Kingdom. ISBN: 978-1-84653-252-8

FSC
www.fsc.org
MIX
Paper from responsible sources
FSC® C010353

MILES MORALES: THE ULTIMATE
SPIDER-MAN
REVIVAL

Greetings, True-Believers!

Welcome to *Marvel Select: Miles Morales: The Ultimate Spider-Man – Revival*. Wow, that title's quite a mouthful. This special edition collects the first seven issues of Miles Morales: The Ultimate Spider-Man into one volume for your instant gratification.

Miles Morales made his debut back in 2011, shortly before the Peter Parker of the Ultimate Marvel Universe was killed in action by the Green Goblin. His run as the web-slinger proved so popular that when Earth-1610 was destroyed during the *Secret Wars* storyline, Miles was one of the few survivors to make the jump into the mainstream Marvel Universe. Since then he's played a major role in *Civil War II*, he's been an Avenger and a founding member of the Champions.

But the *Revival* storyline takes place back when Miles was still figuring out how to be a hero, as he struggled to live up to the responsibility of replacing Peter Parker as Spider-Man. At the risk of divulging a major spoiler, it's got to be said Miles is about to face the biggest challenge of his fledgling career as he goes face-to-face with the man who killed his predecessor, Norman Osborn, better known to fans of mayhem as the Green Goblin!

So, settle down, get comfy, and prepare yourself for a modern-day classic, as we take you with us to Earth-1610 and introduce you to one of the coolest heroes ever to sling a web!

Shortly before Peter Parker was killed by Norman Osborn, the Green Goblin, Miles Morales was bitten by a genetically altered spider that had been stolen from Osborn Industries by his uncle, the Prowler. Miles soon found that the bite had left him with a wide range of incredible spider-like powers.

With Peter Parker dead and Osborn in custody, Miles Morales became the new Spider-Man. Following the death of his mother, Miles decided to walk away from a life of super-heroics, but he soon found himself returning to the role as he teamed up with Spider-Woman, Cloak and Dagger, and Bombshell to take down the evil Roxxon Corporation. He then united with other super-heroes to prevent the cosmic being Galactus from destroying the planet.

In an act of desperation, Miles revealed his secret identity to his father. That was the last time he ever saw him. Now he wants to tell everything to his girlfriend Katie Bishop, a decision his best friend and confidante, Ganke, is sure will bring nothing but trouble.

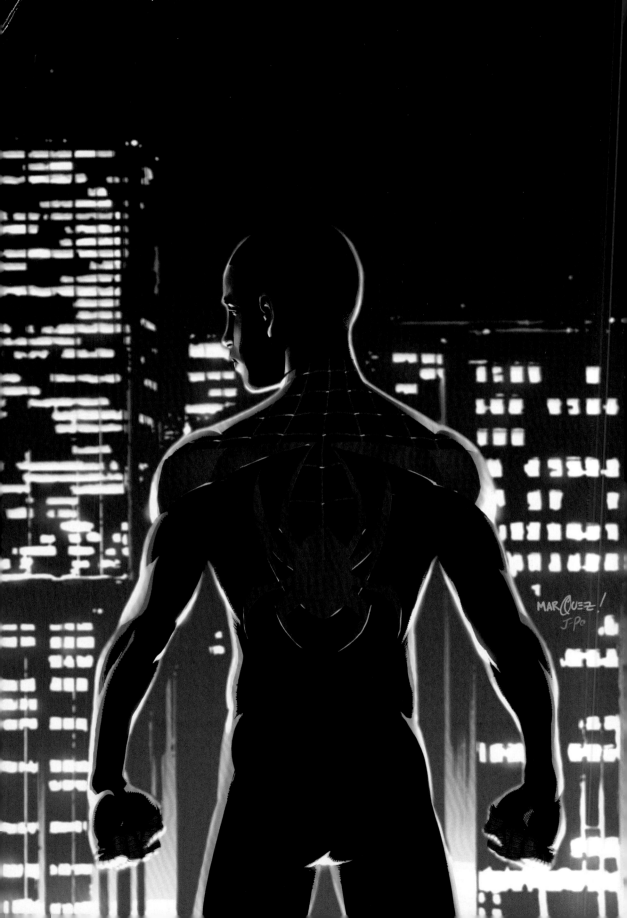

Brooklyn.

He's just taking a break.

He's **not** dead.

Dude. He's dead.

He's taking a break.

That's what the super hero guys do. They take a little break and then they come back.

If it was you or me, we'd be dead.

They had a *funeral* for him!

And I'm sure they did that back in World War II, too.

He was dead in World War II and then he came back. He will come back again.

You are too stupid to function.

He's come back to life before. He's Captain America.

They come back to life when we need them most.

You're annoying me.

Listen, I've studied up on these things.

There is a pattern. It's cyclical.

You're cyclical.

I don't know why it's upsetting you that I have faith in--

Um...

Uh, what do we do?

Um...

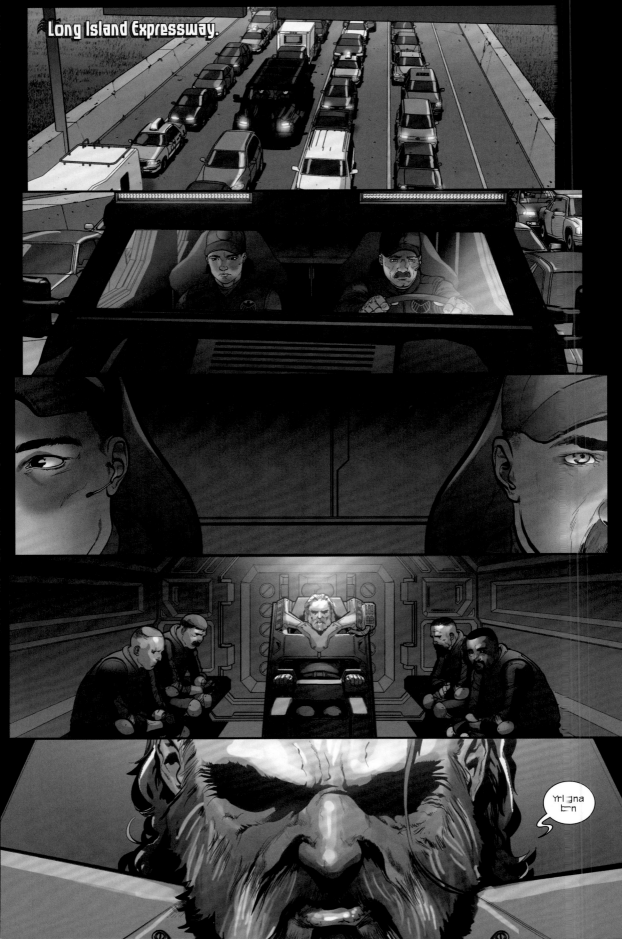

Ganke's House.

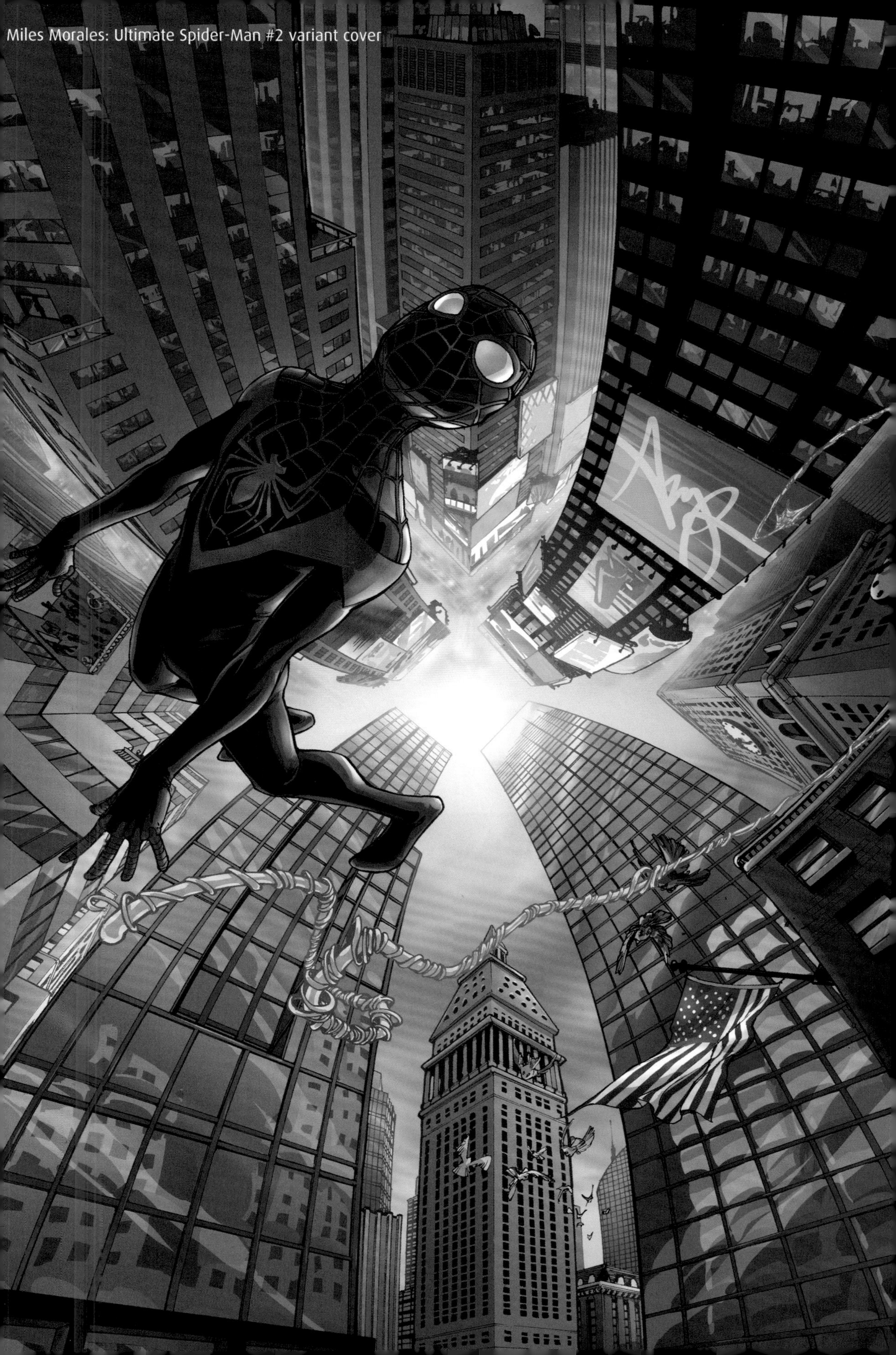

Miles Morales: Ultimate Spider-Man #2 variant cover

Osborn Industries.

Can I have my web-shooters back?

Those, uh, gloves need to be washed.

Can you *hear* me?

I'll wait.

What the #$¢#$¢#$?!

WHAT THE ¢#$¢#$?!

There it is.

Language.

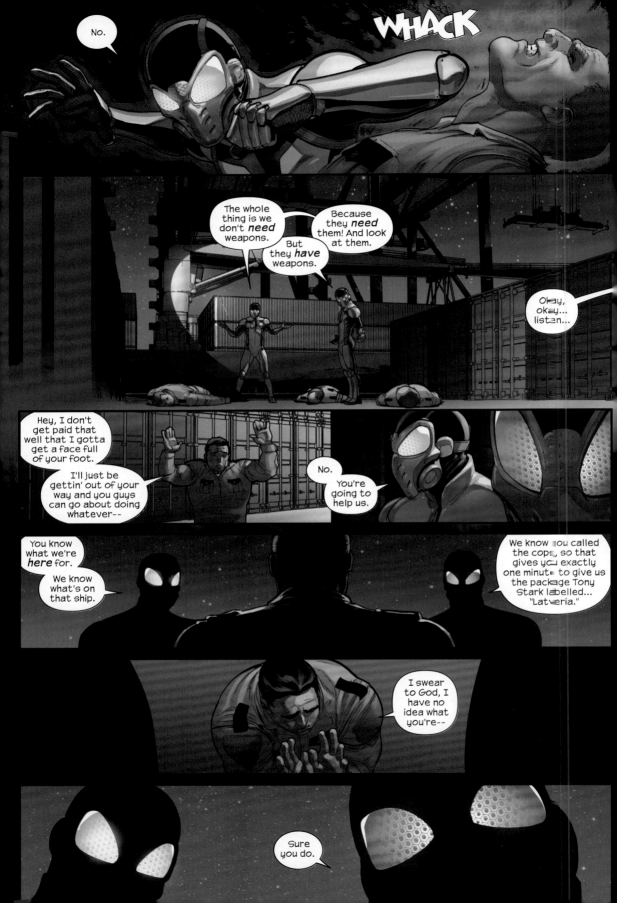

Clone.

Stop saying that, Miles. You're freaking me out.

Ganke...I really need you to believe me.

You need to calm down.

Dude, maybe it *is* him

Maybe Peter Parker *is* alive.

It's a *clone.*

Have you been hit on the head?

Ganke--

Any chance you just dreamt this cr--or imagined this?

You don't believe me.

It's just--give me a second to put it together in my head.

You see how it sounds, right?

Where did this idea even come from?

Okay, I'm going to tell you something but you have to promise me you will never repeat it.

No. But--

You're a clone?

Oh my God. There's a but?

You know The Black Widow? Jessica Drew?

Oh, yeah, I like her. She's--

Before you say she's hot, she's a clone of Peter Parker.

What?

It's a big secret.

She doesn't like to spread it around.

She *told* you this.

Yes.

She's a *clone.*

Yes.

A girl clone.

Yes.

Of Peter Parker.

Yes...

It's two guys dressed up sort of as Spider-Man with some sort of bio-enhancement, maybe powers, terrorizing the city in a crime spree. I want to follow up the story with this video and interview--

Terrorizing?

Do you feel terrorized, Ned?

I do now.

Are you really killing this story?

Killing? No.

I'm not killing your story because there's no story there.

Two guys dressed up and beat up some other guys. We ran that.

You want me to run it again? Find out who they are and what they are up to! Find out what their damn agenda is! File the *story*.

Don't show me blurry clips that are already online...show me a story.

THE SPIDER-MAN MENACE

I'm not spending one more second of our time on salacious half-truth headlines.

I want the whole story!

I know what's behind me. Shut up.

Show me story!

Show me how the death or disappearance of Thor, Captain America and Iron Man has left a vacuum of power amongst the super hero community.

Show me a story about how these new young heroes have risen to the occasion.

Show me something that means something!

Show me something I can use!

Norman Osborn is alive and on the loose!

FBI is running around looking for him even as we speak!

I have it confirmed!

See?

How hard was that?

Police Station.

I can't believe you federales.

You shut down S.H.I.E.L.D., which would have been able to handle this no problem...

And then you drag me into court to blame me for everything that's wrong with the world and now you want my help with this!

You are still a salaried employee of the federal government, former S.H.I.E.L.D. Director Chang.

Hey, uh, just call me Monica.

Let's go on this wild goose chase then.

Yes. You do.

But, if you knew anything about anything, you'd know you send low-level grunts to do the low-level grunt work...

You don't spend $85 million on decommissioned Hulkbuster armor to crash a long abandoned laboratory.

(I don't care how many Spider-Men were accidentally created here.)

Uh, someone has been in here.

There's substantial fire damage.

This is recent.

This is hardly a wild goose chase. Norman Osborn is on the loose.

And, trust me, this is the last place you will find Norman Osborn.

The very last place on Earth.

But we have to look.

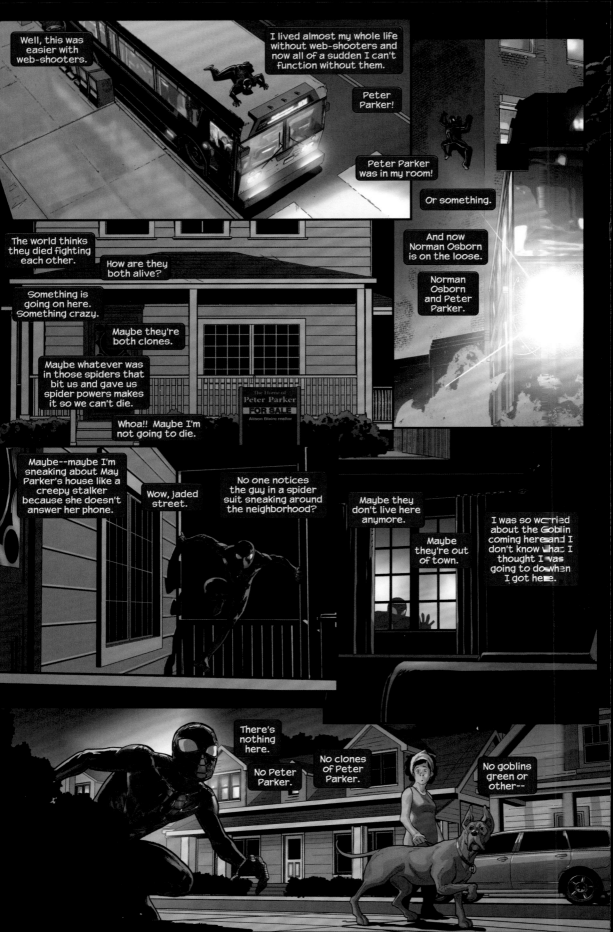

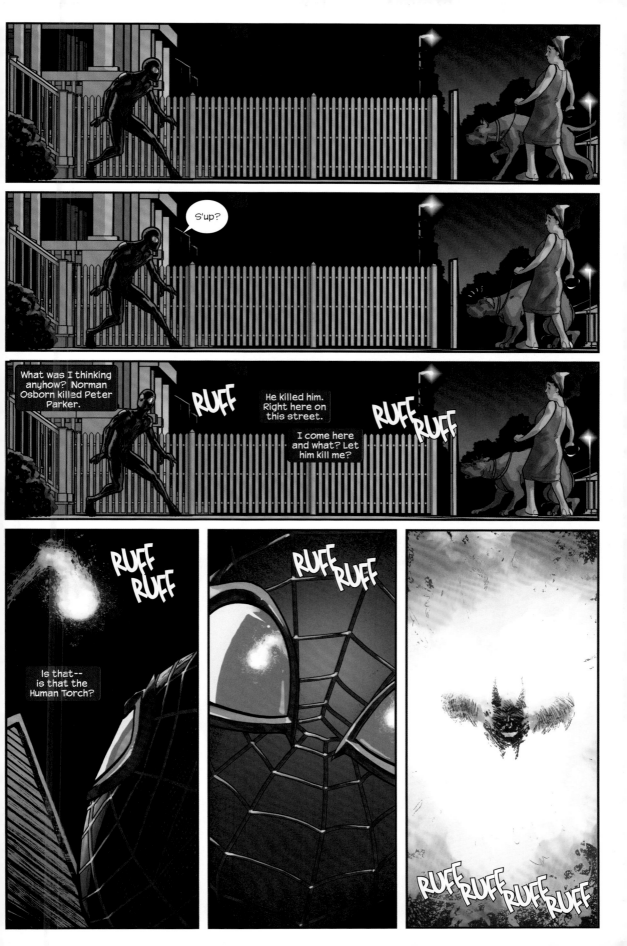

What? For real?

For real!

Is this something you're guessing?

He flat out told me.

Oh my God.

Yeah.

Oh my God!

Yeah.

Katie, you can't tell mom and dad.

I know.

If you like this guy even a little...you have to break up with him and you can never tell them.

I know.

I don't want to break up with him and even if I do break up with him, he loves me as much as I love him and he's going to do something stupid to try to get me back!

He told you he was Spider-Man?

The new-ish Spider-Man?

Yes!

Why would he do that?

Because he loves me. Because he wanted to trust me. What-- what am I going to do?

Hope that a super villain kills him?

That-- that's an awful thing to say.

Hey! That's the best case scenario.

What?!

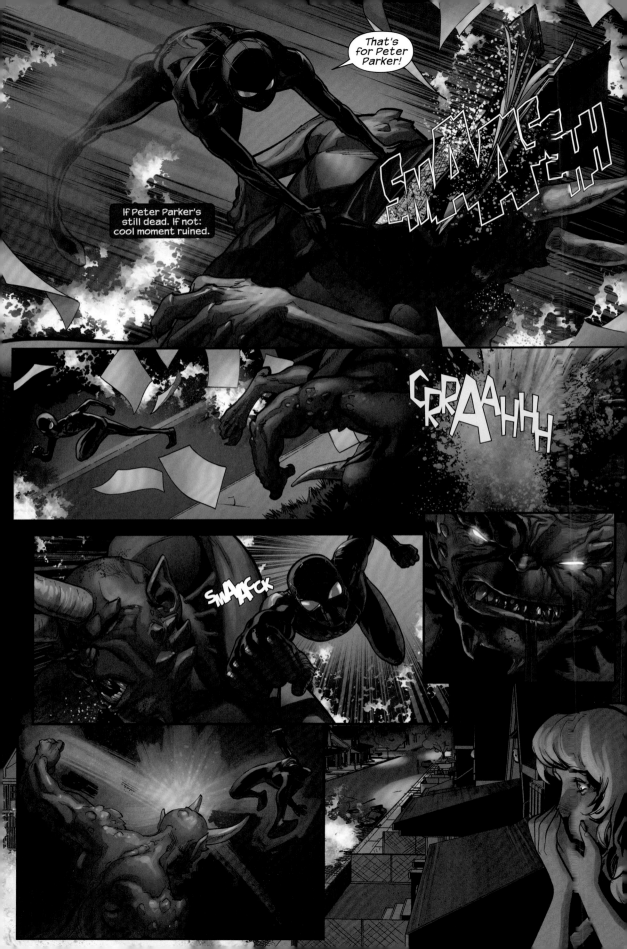

Numerous calls coming in from the Forest Hills neighborhood reporting Spider-Man--
And what may or may not be the Green Goblin--
Ganke, Best Friend.
Detective Maria Hill.
Ben Urich, Reporter.
The damage to the neighborhood is already severe.
If you are anywhere near this area, please stay in your home and stay off the streets.
FASHHAM
We are still waiting for confirmation that this is in fact Norman Osborn, once a well-respected member of the military-industrial complex and now--
Rumors of Osborn's escape from prison seem to be true.
Details are sketchy as to how this new Spider-Man and Osborn have come to find each other--
Neighborhood alerts! Super-power event sighting! Stay in your home! This is not a test.
Interestingly enough, this is exactly the location where Peter Parker last battled the Green Goblin and eventually lost his life.
J. Jonah Jameson, Daily Bugle Publisher.
Mary Jane Watson, Original Spider-Man Girlfriend.
Katie Bishop, Miles Morales' soon to be ex-girlfriend.
Aunt May and Gwen Stacy, Peter Parker's only remaining family.

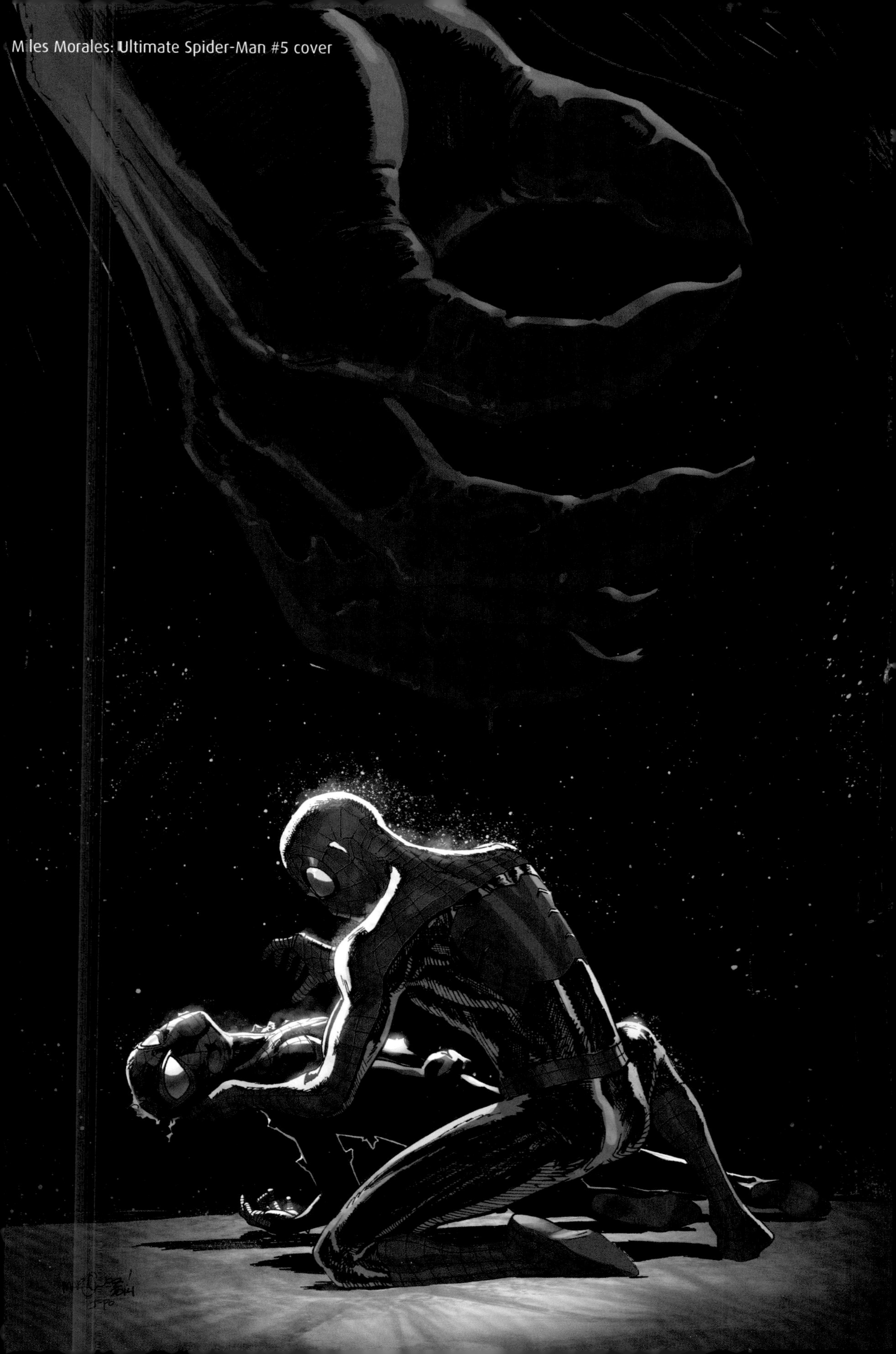

The Home of Peter Parker.
Queens, New York.

NO SHOTS FIRED!

I repeat, I am Captain Frank Quaid of NYPD and there will be *no shots fired!*

That is a very good idea!

Is there someone you can call to stop this?

Who? Like the police?

No, we're going to have to do this the old-fashioned way.

There's an old-fashioned way?

Spider, uh, men...you need to take off your masks and lie on the ground, on your belly, arms out!

This is no game!

You know how to get out of something like this, right?

I did before you stole my web-shooters.

They're my web-shooters.

They were a present.

Masks off, boys! I mean it!

I don't want your blood on my hands.

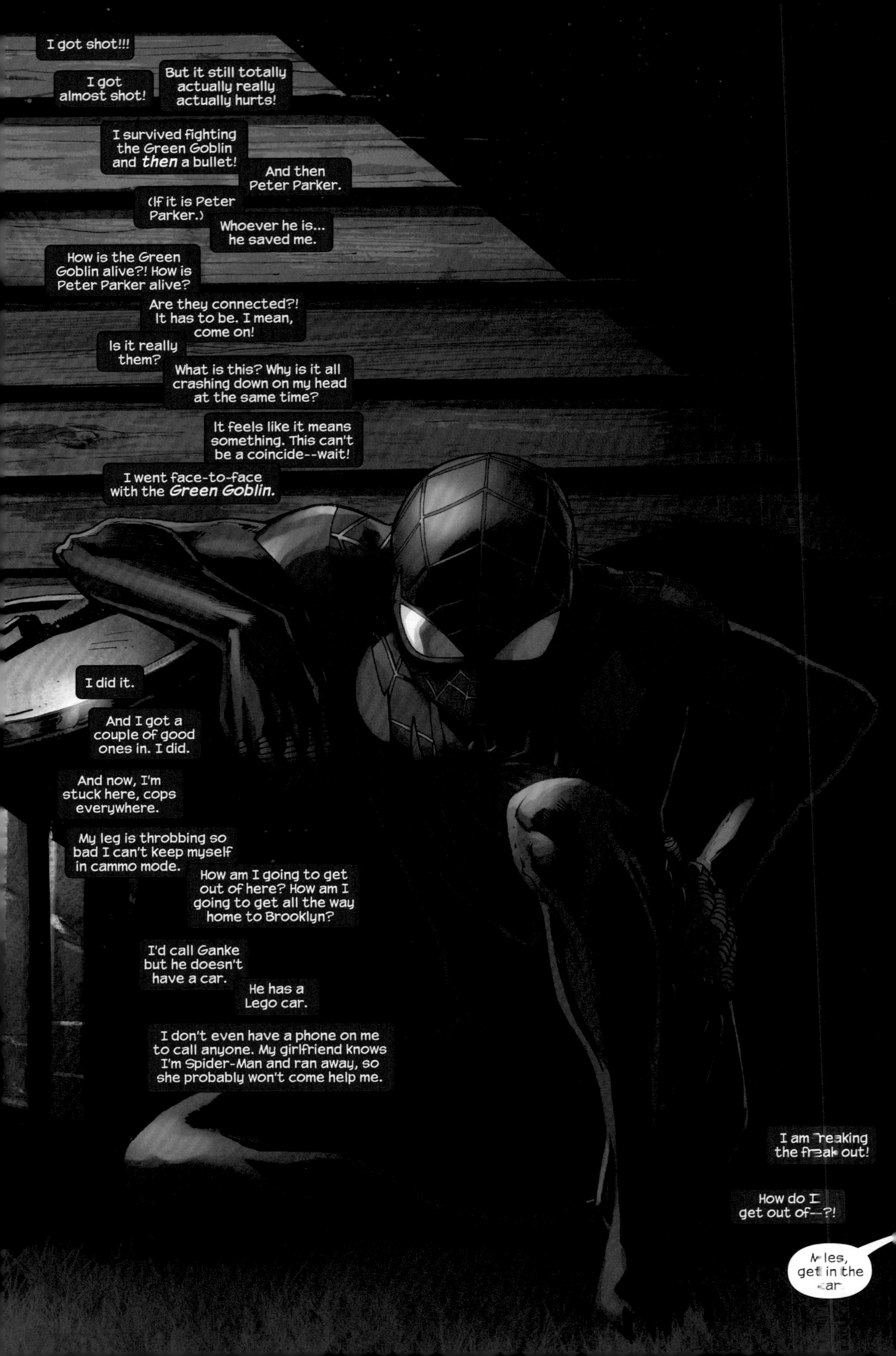
I got shot!!!
I got almost shot!
But it still totally actually really actually hurts!
I survived fighting the Green Goblin and *then* a bullet!
And then Peter Parker.
(If it is Peter Parker.)
Whoever he is... he saved me.
How is the Green Goblin alive?! How is Peter Parker alive?
Are they connected?! It has to be. I mean, come on!
Is it really them?
What is this? Why is it all crashing down on my head at the same time?
It feels like it means something. This can't be a coincide--wait!
I went face-to-face with the *Green Goblin.*
I did it.
And I got a couple of good ones in. I did.
And now, I'm stuck here, cops everywhere.
My leg is throbbing so bad I can't keep myself in cammo mode.
How am I going to get out of here? How am I going to get all the way home to Brooklyn?
I'd call Ganke but he doesn't have a car.
He has a Lego car.
I don't even have a phone on me to call anyone. My girlfriend knows I'm Spider-Man and ran away, so she probably won't come help me.
I am freaking the freak out!
How do I get out of--?!
Miles, get in the car.

LIVE! SPIDER-MEN BATTLE SCENE. NYPD HAVE THEM SURROUNDED.

GNN

Dude, you're missing it.

GOBLIN BATTLES SPIDER-MEN IN QUEENS... NYPD IN STANDO

Oh my God.

It's like a--it's a sign.

LIVE GNN

ENS...NYPD IN S_ _TH REVIVED PETER PA

A sign of what?

Two Spider-Men. Right now. In Queens. Fighting the police.

Old one is dead. No?

We're going out.

Now? I just showered.

We're in the middle of a world-class, headline-grabbing crime spree that the media is half-blaming on Spider-Man.

We'll head to Midtown and cross another item off our list.

It is not our list.

It is our task.

I think we're pushing our luck.

Maybe because of us.

Two?

That new one and one that kind of looks like the old one.

Get dressed.

Why?

All the cops in the city will be chasing them...

...the least we could do is take full advantage of it.

H REV

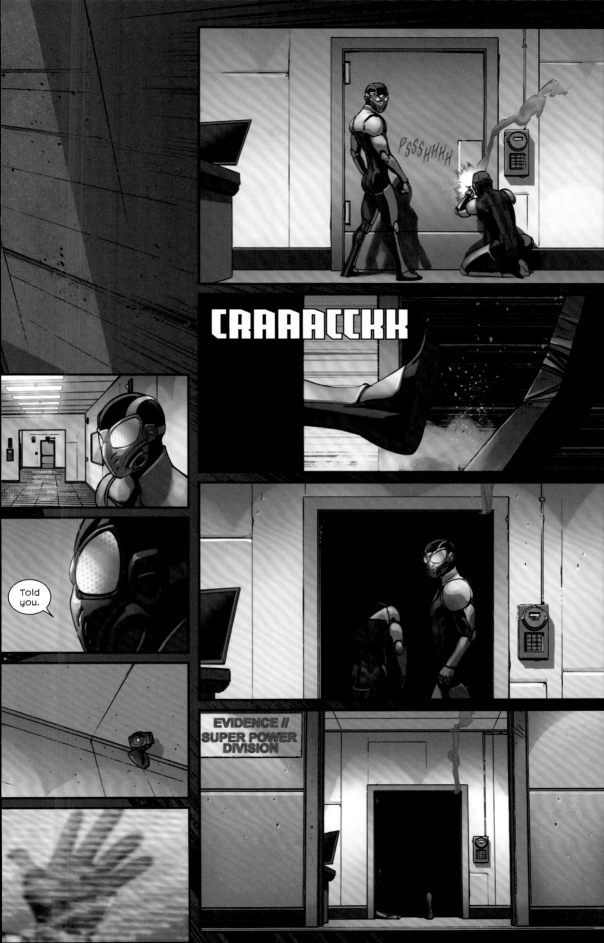

Oh, dear
God, what have
I done?

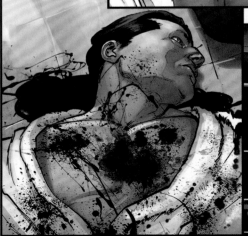

BEEP
BOOP
BEEP
BEEP
BOOP

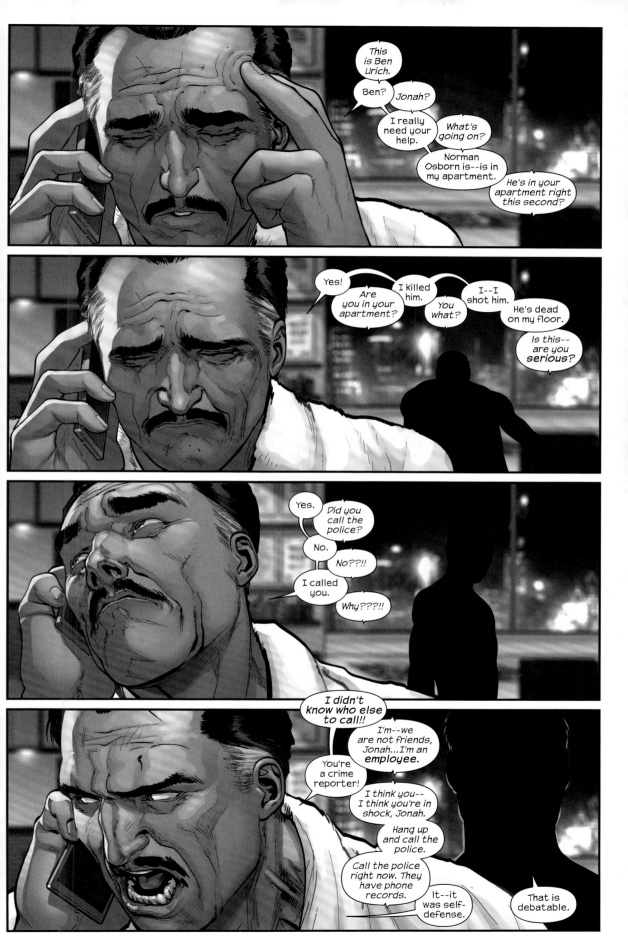

"I remember everything.

"Everything that happened in my entire life.

"I remember my entire life and I remember my death.

"And then...

"I woke up...

"In darkness.

"I woke up in a lab.

"The entire thing abandoned.

"Like everyone just got up and ran out.

"Was it Roxxon? Was it S.H.I.E.L.D.? Oscorp?

"For a second, I thought it was the end of the world and I was the only survivor.

"There was literally no way to tell.

"The computers were all wiped.

"All data pulled or deleted.

"I had no idea how I got from dead to here.

"All I knew was that I was somewhere outside Atlanta and I had a lot of buses and trucks to stow away on top of before I could get back to New York."

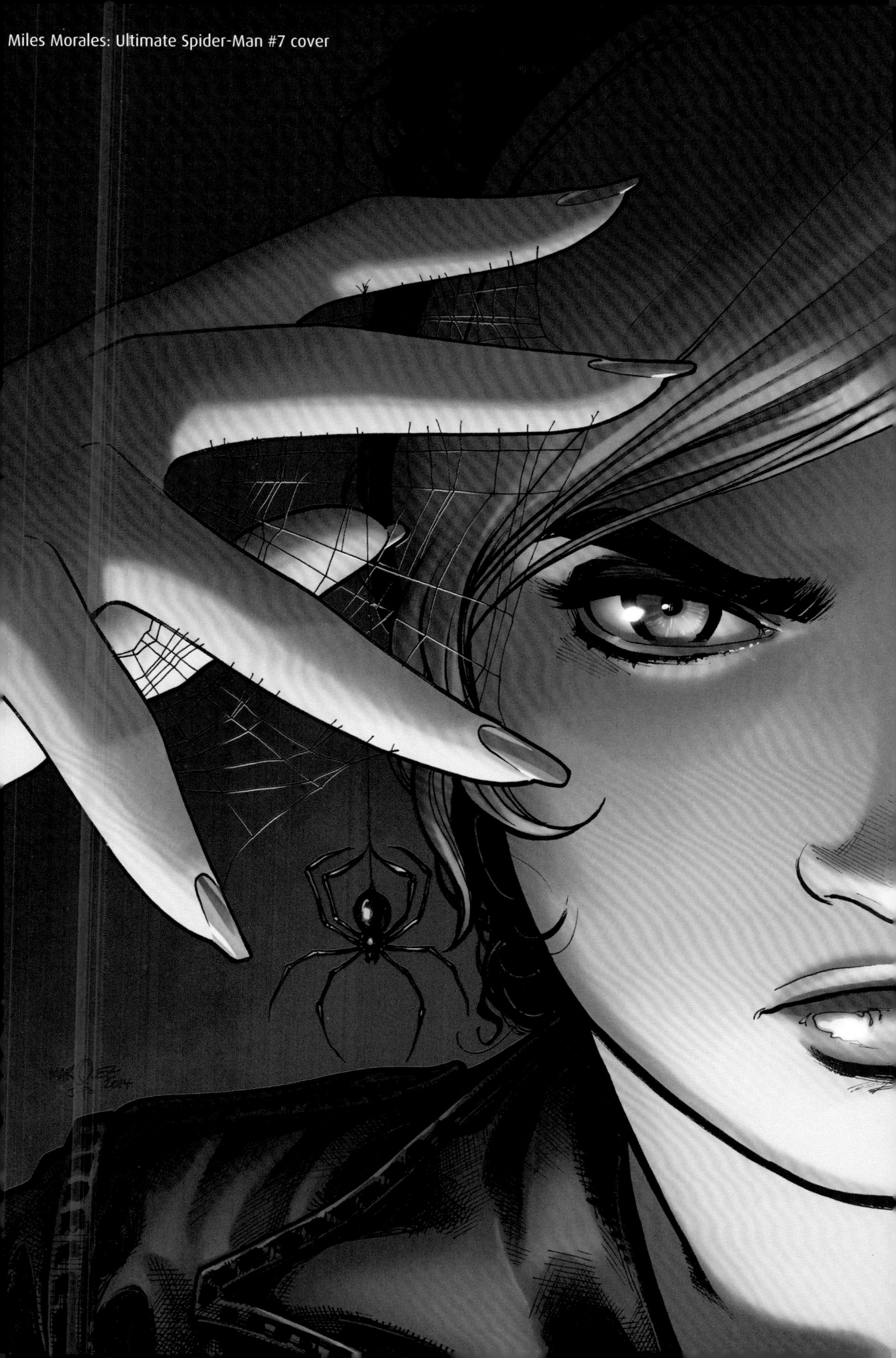

The Home Of Mary Jane Watson.

Yo, Miles. You really gotta get up.

Yeah, well, you really gotta get up.

C'mon, Ganke, I had a rough night.

You have a--you have a visitor.

Oh my God...

DAD!

Hey, boy...

I believe you and I need to talk.

Ultimate Spider-Man #200 cover